THE PEDDLER'S DREAM

The Peddler's Dream
and other Plays

BY

JAMES REEVES

WITH AN INTRODUCTION BY
Nellie McCaslin
MILLS COLLEGE OF EDUCATION

E. P. DUTTON & CO., INC., NEW YORK

TO
STELLA

First published in the U.S.A., 1963 by E. P. Dutton & Co., Inc.

Copyright, ©, 1963 by E. P. Dutton & Co., Inc.
All rights reserved. Printed in the U.S.A.

FIRST EDITION

Library of Congress Catalog Card Number: 63-8592

CONTENTS

INTRODUCTION

The three plays in this volume are a delightful contribution to the all too limited supply of good plays for young players. Mr. Reeves has suggested that they are particularly suitable for boys and girls from ten to fourteen. In this recommendation I should concur most heartily. I should, however, consider them equally appropriate and worthwhile for high school and adult producing groups.

Folk tales know no age level for the obvious reason that such material has been enjoyed by young and old alike for countless generations. Through the telling and retelling these stories have acquired a rare simplicity, retaining what is universal and true to human nature and shedding details which are temporal or superfluous. Although the folk tale has a regional origin, its counterpart is frequently to be found in another locale, suggesting that it is the characters and behavior which are of primary concern. Two of the three plays in this collection are based on folk material. The third is not but might well be for the characteristics it shares with the other two.

Mr. Reeves has made use of simple plots which are direct and forward moving. Dramatic action takes place on stage rather than off, a quality particularly important in the play for young people. His characters, like those in the folk tale or legend, are clear-cut with human qualities which can be easily understood and appreciated. Basic motives and values emerge through comic or dramatic situations. His humor is universal, thus appealing to persons of all ages. Because of his respect for young people, he has neither written down nor over-simplified his vocabulary. For these reasons his work should be welcomed by both inexperienced and advanced groups of players.

As Mr. Reeves points out in his Preface, stage production is not an important consideration. All three plays can be performed on a bare stage if necessary, with a mere suggestion of costume. Should the director wish to produce them more elaborately, he will find a rich opportunity. None of the plays, however, depends upon technical tricks or lavish staging for its effectiveness.

Because the characters are primarily human beings, rather than natives of a particular province, dialect may be introduced or omitted. Again, it is character rather than mode of speech which is important.

I should think all three plays excellent for both classroom or workshop use and public presentation. Like all good plays, they command the interest of participants and audience. We are fortunate, therefore, in having this collection of plays of superior quality available for American production.

Nellie McCaslin

Director of Dramatic Arts,
Mills College of Education in New York City

PREFACE

These plays have been written especially for the entertainment of young people between the ages of ten and fourteen, as readers, as actors or as spectators. I have tried to avoid the difficulties of adult plays and the condescension only too common in children's plays. No situations are introduced which are beyond the acting powers of young people. But the young like acting adult parts, and adult emotions of simple kinds have been represented. I have tried to make the situations concrete, factual and dramatic, and to portray a wide range of characters.

No particular dialect has been suggested and none is necessary, but any regional dialect, provided it is not too obviously urban, would not be out of place. Moreover, there is scope for playing in costume, so that the wardrobe department will take an active share in production.

Settings, costume, speech and gesture should alike be simple, bold, suggestive rather than representational—in short, what is most truly theatrical will on the stage be most effective. Stage directions are given sparingly for the most part, because invention and ingenuity on the part of the director are the life blood of dramatic activity. In two of the plays songs are included and melodies suggested. If the songs or melodies are unacceptable to actors or director, let others be adapted or made up. The director must take any

9

liberties with the text which he thinks warranted, according to the capacities of his players and his scenic resources, provided he does his best to interpret the dramatic intention of the plays. For instance, in the first play I have characterized one of the rogues by giving him a slight stammer. With some young players it may be thought desirable to omit this.

Finally, although these plays are written for amateurs, they will be best enjoyed if undertaken with professional seriousness. A successful production depends on the careful co-ordination of a mass of details. There is not one in a dramatic production, however humble his function, who cannot ruin the performance by some small fault. The educational significance of this truth is self evident. These are apprentice plays, brief and unassuming, but their presentation will involve most of the problems encountered in much more ambitious productions.

James Reeves

THE PEDDLER'S DREAM

✦   ✦   ✦

The Players

MARTIN, the Peddler
MARGERY, his wife
GILLIAN, his daughter
OLD MAN
FIRST WOMAN
SECOND WOMAN
THIRD WOMAN
FOURTH WOMAN
FIRST MAN
SECOND MAN
THIRD MAN
GENTLEMAN

✦   ✦

ACT I

The village of Mulbridge. The living room in the Peddler's cottage. Breakfast time. A window at the back; in front of it a bench and in front of this a table. There is a door leading outside. The Peddler's wife MARGERY *and his daughter* GILLIAN *are putting dishes on the table for breakfast.* MARGERY *is a shrewd, careful housewife of forty.* GILLIAN, *aged twenty, is pretty, but not silly.*

GILLIAN: Where's father?

MARGERY: Gone up the road to get some cider.

GILLIAN: Is not the home brew good enough for him, then?

MARGERY: There is none left, daughter. And precious little to eat either. We are near starving.

GILLIAN: Is trade that bad, mother?

MARGERY: Trade is always bad for poor peddlers. Specially in winter when roads are bad and there are no travelers, and fairs are few and far between.

GILLIAN: Well, there is milk here, and bread, and good porridge. That's enough for any man.

MARGERY: Your father is going out on the road, child; and when he goes traveling he must have good cider inside him—so he says; but cider or no cider, your father will ever be a simple soul, Jill.

GILLIAN: Father's a good man, mother, though he be but a poor peddler.

MARGERY: Don't I know it? I that have been married to him for over twenty years. If he were not such a good man, maybe he would be cleverer at making money, and I should not have to be so clever making a Sunday dinner out of two cabbage leaves and a scraggy bone that'd make a very skeleton ashamed.

GILLIAN (*laughing*): It's not so bad as that, mother.

But why is father going on the roads this time of the year?

MARGERY: Father has had one of his dreams.

GILLIAN: A dream? Why what dream has father had this time?

MARGERY: I know not. Ask him yourself. All I know is that his dream tells him he must be out on the road and leave his wife and only daughter to feed on cast-off shoe leather and puppy dogs' tails.

GILLIAN: Do you remember his last dream, mother? —How he was one of Robin Hood's merry men and I was his daughter Marian——

MARGERY: Yes, and he made himself a bow and arrow and shot one of Farmer Crumbock's fat cows in the buttock, and Farmer Crumbock had him fined five shillings for he said the cow was frightened near to death. And do you remember his other dream when he dreamed——

The Peddler is seen passing the window with a jug of cider. He is singing.

GILLIAN: Hush, mother, here he comes.

Enter MARTIN the Peddler. He sets down the jug on the table and prepares to sit down on the bench under the window.

MARTIN:

Fortune, fortune!
Hear the bells of London town,

Silken hose and velvet gown.
Fortune, fortune!
Wheel go up and wheel come down.

What's for breakfast, Madge my dear? Here is a jug of Mother Crabtree's cider that she has let me have for no money, against the time I bring home my fortune. For I told her my dream.

MARGERY: Enough of your dream for now, husband, and eat your breakfast. You may well sing for it, for here is bread that is seven days old and porridge that might gladden the hearts of Farmer Crumbock's swine.

GILLIAN *hands round porridge and bread.* MARTIN *pours out cider. All sit and eat during the following conversation.*

MARTIN: It's very good bread and very good porridge, but is there no bacon, my dear?

MARGERY: The bacon is kept for your journey, for you are not going on the road this day without food in your pack. A foolish man you may be, but you shall not starve.

MARTIN: You are too good for me, Madge, and I am a poor, unworthy husband. Moreover, so fair you are that it is a wonder someone has not run away with you before now.

MARGERY: Fie upon you, you seller of ballads!

MARTIN: But it is no wonder you are fair, being the

FORTUNE

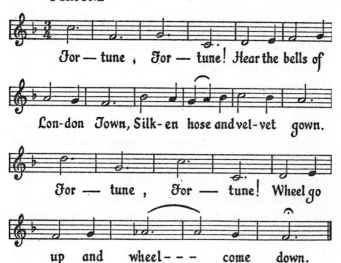

For — tune , For — tune! Hear the bells of Lon-don Town, Silk-en hose and vel-vet gown. For — tune , For — tune! Wheel go up and wheel - - - come down.

mother of my sweet daughter Gillian. Are you well this morning, Jill, and have you slept soundly?

GILLIAN: Yes, father, for I am not troubled with foolish dreams like some I could name.

MARTIN: Well, I will tell you the dream I dreamed last night, now that I have some of Mistress Crabtree's cider inside me. It was like this.

MARGERY: I will have none of your stupid dreams this morning, for do we not know that they come only from eating pickled cabbage and salt fish? No, you must first hear what I have to say to you.

MARTIN: Say on, wife of the foolishest man that ever

peddled laces and ribbons for silly girls to buy at markets.

MARGERY: If there were no silly girls wanting ribbons to be married in and ballads to sing upon their wedding day, you and I would starve.

MARTIN: That is true. You are a wise woman, as wise as I am foolish. (*He drinks.*) Long life to maids, say I. May they live to be married a score of times! And all buy their caps and ribbons from Martin the Peddler!

MARGERY: It is of màrriage that I want to talk with you, husband—and of your daughter.

GILLIAN (*rising*): No, mother, do not trouble father with that now. It can wait.

MARGERY: Quiet, child. Go into the other room and begin sorting the dirty linen, for you know it's washing day; and before your father goes off to take up his new place as Emperor of China, I would talk to him about the affairs of his own family.

GILLIAN (*going*): Very well, mother, I will do as you say.

She goes out.

MARGERY: It is about Jill, husband. She is turned twenty and wants to marry.

MARTIN: Why should she want to marry? She has a good home here. This is as snug a cottage as she will find in all Mulbridge.

MARGERY: And that is small thanks to you, for the

cottage is mine. 'Twas given me by my father's brother when my mother died. 'Twas here I was living with my father when you came along with your taking ways and pretty ballads, Martin. I had no money, then, and have had none since.

MARTIN: Yes, it's strange, for 'twas said your uncle had gold, but there was none when he died.

MARGERY: Well, it's no good crying over a cracked dish. Our daughter does not want to live with her mother and father and sort out the dirty linen to the end of her days. She wants to marry and——

MARTIN: And have dirty linen of her own, I dare say. For all women must wash linen, whether it be their own or another's. But what shall she do for a husband? She cannot marry Goodman Crumbock's son, for he is silly, and besides he is married already.

MARGERY: She is to marry Simon the wheelwright's son who lives by the mill on the Mulcaster Road, as well you know.

MARTIN: Yes, to be sure. Simon is a good boy, though he has not two pennies to jingle together.

MARGERY: That is just it, you blockhead! Nor has our Gillian any dresses nor shoes nor house linen nor dishes nor cocks and hens to bring to her husband like a respectable girl should. She has nothing but her wooden clogs and her old woolen smock. You would not have her married in these?

MARTIN: No, indeed. She must have fine linen and laces to go to church with—and pewter dishes and twelve cocks and hens, if you say so wife; and a fat sow with a litter of nine porkers would not be too good for her, either.

MARGERY: I am glad you understand, husband. But where is the money to come from for these things? Or have you dreamed that they are to be found floating in a ship on the Red Sea and you have only to go and fish for them?

MARTIN (*seriously*): Well, not exactly. But have the girl come in and I will tell you both what it is I have dreamed. Gillian!

MARGERY: Gillian, come in!

GILLIAN *comes back.*

Your father has consented that you shall be wed to Simon the wheelwright's son——

GILLIAN: Oh, thank you, father! (*She kisses him.*)

MARGERY: And now he is going to tell us how he will provide gold dishes for you to eat from and a silken gown to sit in of a morning and do your embroidery, while twelve servants wait upon you and cook your meals.

GILLIAN: Oh, father, I don't want gold dishes, but only a few things for the house and a dress or two and some shoes and a woolen quilt to keep us warm in winter.

MARTIN: Well, my dears, the other night I dreamed a dream, and in my dream a fellow came to me who was dressed like a lawyer and spoke to me. And this is what he said—

MARGERY: "You must go to prison," says he, "for not paying for your peddler's license."

MARTIN: Do not interrupt, wife, or I shall forget where I was. Now, where was I? Oh yes. This fellow that was dressed like a parson——

MARGERY: It was like a lawyer just now.

GILLIAN: Quiet, mother, I beg you.

MARTIN: Did I say a lawyer? Well, it's all one, for he was like a lawyer and like a parson, you know how it is in dreams. This fellow said to me, "Go to London Bridge," says he, "and stand on London Bridge forty days, and there you shall make your fortune." "Make my fortune," says I. "How may that be?"

MARGERY: And what did the fellow say?

MARTIN: That I cannot tell, my dear, for it was then that you woke me up with putting your elbow in my ribs. "Time to get up and bring in logs," you said. So my dream ended and I know not how my fortune shall be made. But to London I will go this day, my wife. Is my pack ready?

MARGERY *and* GILLIAN (*together*): To London!

MARTIN: Yes, to London. And I must start now, for the days are short and I must be far away by nightfall. Go and get my pack, Jill.

GILLIAN: But father——

GILLIAN *goes out*.

MARGERY: No, go not to London, my dear. When you told me you were going upon the road, I thought 'twas only to Mulcaster or maybe Normanbury. But London is a long way.

MARTIN: To London I must go, Madge. For 'twas on London Bridge that this fellow said I was to find my fortune.

GILLIAN *comes in with the pack*.

And how shall my little Jill have her wedding dress if I do not make my fortune?

GILLIAN: My wedding can wait, father. At the summer fairs perhaps you will make enough money. Do not go to London.

MARGERY: Remember my father, Martin. I have neither father nor mother now. I do not want to lose husband as well, foolish as you are.

MARTIN: Ah, your father, my dear. What of him? Did he dream a dream?

MARGERY: I do not know. But after my uncle died and left us a cottage and no money, he also went to London to seek his fortune, and none of us has ever seen him since.

MARTIN: Well, God send me better fortune. Come now, do not cry. I have left you twelve pennies to get you food till I return. What a day that will be! (*He takes up his pack.*) Come, help me on with my pack, Jill. What is there in it besides food for my journey?

MARGERY: There are four dozen clothespins, some ribbons and a score of laces, a dozen or so handkerchiefs, some little pins made of tin that will pass for silver, and the new ballad of the crocodile that was found by the fisherman on the Goodwin Sands, and a new pair of wool stockings that I have made for you out of scarlet wool.

GILLIAN: How long will you be gone, father?

MARTIN: Forty days, unless I find my fortune sooner.

He sings.

> Fortune, fortune!
> Hear the bells of London Town——

No, do not cry, Madge. Come, kiss me and let me be gone. Good-by, Jill, and may the Lord keep you both.

MARGERY: Good-by, Martin, may the Lord keep you for you will never keep yourself.

GILLIAN: Good-by, dear father. God go with you; do not forget to wear the woolen stockings when your feet are cold. (*She kisses him.*)

MARTIN: Good-by to you both. (*He goes out singing as they stand at the door waving and calling* "Good-by, my love." "Good-by, father.")

> Silken hose and velvet gown,
>   Fortune, fortune!

Wheel go up and wheel come down.

After a pause MARGERY *picks up dishes, etc.*

MARGERY: Ah well, there is work to be done. Come don't stand there idling. Take out some of these dishes and then fetch me the linen.

GILLIAN *goes, taking dishes.*

Let foolish men go seek their fortunes, but for us women it's always washing day.

She begins piling up the remaining dishes.

ACT 2

London Bridge, seven weeks later. On a ladder or other convenient place raised a little above the pavement stands MARTIN *with his pack of wares. He is wearing his red stockings.*

MARTIN: Come, who'll buy pins, laces or ribbons for their caps?

Enter two WOMEN *with baskets over their arms.*

Come, mistress, will you not buy a ribbon or a pretty handkerchief?

Enter slowly an OLD MAN *with a stick and a little*

cup for begging. He stands at one side looking on.

1ST WOMAN: Let me see some ribbons, fellow.

2ND WOMAN: And let me see what handkerchiefs you have.

MARTIN *shows them his wares.*

MARTIN: Here you are, mistress. Fine cambric handkerchiefs and ribbons of blue, yellow and red.

1ST WOMAN: These are poor goods, Master Peddler. These are fit only for tying up horses' tails.

2ND WOMAN: These handkerchiefs are not so bad. How much for one of these, Peddler.

MARTIN: They are sixpence apiece.

2ND WOMAN: Nay, that is too dear.

MARTIN: Well, I will let you have two of them for tenpence, but in truth I can go no lower. They cost me that to buy.

2ND WOMAN: They are too dear for me. I can get as good in Islington Fair.

1ST WOMAN: I do not like your ribbons either. Take them back.

MARTIN: Have you no need of pins, nor clothespins, nor a proper new ballad entitled——

1ST WOMAN: Nay, fellow, I have no need of ballads. Come, neighbor, we shall be late for the butter market.

2ND WOMAN: And I must get dried fish for my husband's dinner.

The women go off talking. The OLD MAN *has come slowly up to* MARTIN.

MARTIN: Now, sir, what will you have? Laces for your shoes or garters for your hose?

OLD MAN: No, Peddler, for I have no shoes and scarce any hose. I am an old man and poor and I am forced to beg for bread.

MARTIN: Oh, I beg your pardon, old man. But alas, I have no bread to give. Here is a penny that I had this morning from a boy who bought——

OLD MAN: No, I want no money from you, for I see you are as poor as I am. I want but to sit down upon the pavement beside you for the sake of your company.

MARTIN: Welcome, father. Sit down, and watch how I make my fortune. (OLD MAN *sits down slowly*.) For I am to stand here forty days, and today is the fortieth. Yet I do not like London; the folks are too clever for a country fellow like me.

OLD MAN: Ah, Peddler, 'twas many years ago that I came up to this city of London to make my fortune, but fortune passed me by. Folks here, as you say, are clever, and they are wise too and do not give away money to make poor beggars' fortunes. But how have you fared?

MARTIN: As you see, old man. These folks want none of my wares.

Enter a little gathering of men and women, the first one or two beckoning the others.

1ST MAN: Here is a peddler, neighbors. Let us see what he has. Come, Cis, I will buy you a ribbon if you will let me kiss you.

2ND MAN: Let him sing us a ballad.

3RD WOMAN: Have you a kerchief, fellow, so that I may cover my head?

1ST MAN: Let it be big enough to cover her face too!

3RD MAN: Have you a bloodthirsty ballad of a Spaniard that has his throat cut?

2ND MAN: This fellow is from the country and will give us a country song that will make us all laugh.

ALL: Yes, a song, a song!

MARTIN: Will you have the new ballad of the crocodile that was found by a fisherman on the Goodwin Sands?

1ST MAN: No, we will have no crocodile, lest we weep crocodile tears. (*Laughter.*)

MARTIN: Will you have the song of Fortune, then, or the song of Mad Margaret? No, I will sing you the song of Golden Hair, and everyone that likes this song shall give a penny to this old man.

During this speech a GENTLEMAN, *middle-aged and rather elegant, comes in. He stands to one side and looks on with amusement.*

ALL: Yes, Golden Hair, Golden Hair! Sing us Golden Hair!

3RD WOMAN: What if we do not like the song, master peddler?

MARTIN: Why, then, you must give two pennies for charity. (*He sings.*)

> As I do walk now here, now there,
>   With hey, the bonny eglantine.
> To take the wholesome country air,
>   With hey, the bonny eglantine.
> My feet they wander everywhere.
> But my heart goes not with me,
> For see my love, it stays with thee,
>   Golden Hair, Golden Hair,
>   Tangled in thy golden hair.
> And hey, the eglantine is bonny.

Applause and some laughter.

1ST MAN: This country fellow does not sing badly.

3RD WOMAN: A pretty song, indeed.

2ND MAN: Ah, how sweetly you sing, master musician. You have made me so sad that for two pins I would throw myself over London Bridge into the river here.

MARTIN (*searching in his pack*): Why, sir, here are the two pins, take them, and let us see you do what you say you will.

Laughter. Everyone is amused by the peddler's joke.

1ST MAN: Yes, yes, jump in the river, friend!

ALL: Jump in the river! He has given you the two pins, do as you said.

MARTIN: Well, if you will not wet yourself, sir, will you pay a forfeit?

GOLDEN HAIR

As I do walk now here now there, With hey, the bon-ny

e-glan-tine. To take the whole-some coun-try air, With hey the bon-ny

e-glan-tine My feet they wan-der ev'-ry where, But my heart goes

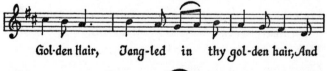

not with me, For see my love, it stays with thee, Gol-den Hair,

Gol-den Hair, Tang-led in thy gol-den hair, And

hey, the e — glan-tine — is bon-ny —.

ALL: Ay, a forfeit, a forfeit!

MARTIN: You must buy these two silver pins for sixpence each.

2ND MAN: Very good, fellow. Here are your two sixpences. Give me the pins. (*He takes them.*) Why,
these are not silver. These are tin.

MARTIN: Ay, sir, these are good white tin. You have
had your joke and I must have mine. (*Laughter.*)
Come, worthy citizens, who'll buy laces, ribbons
and handkerchiefs? Who'll buy?

4TH WOMAN: No, I must be going. I have work to do.

She gives a penny to the OLD MAN *and goes out.
The rest follow her laughing, talking, and some
singing the air of Golden Hair. Some give coins to
the* OLD MAN. MARTIN *is left with the* OLD MAN
and the GENTLEMAN, *who comes forward to talk
to him. He speaks in a languid and foppish tone.*

GENTLEMAN: Tell me, fellow, you cause much mer-
riment, but do you make any money?

MARTIN: Alas, no, sir. These London folk are fond of
a joke but they are not fond of laying out money.

GENTLEMAN: I have seen you stand in this same place
for many weeks. Why do you do this?

MARTIN: Well, sir, I have had a dream.

GENTLEMAN: A dream?

MARTIN: Yes, sir.

GENTLEMAN: Tell me your dream, fellow.

MARTIN: I am a poor peddler, sir, who lives in a village far away near the city of Mulcaster, and I dreamed that if I came to London and stood on the bridge here for forty days, I should make my fortune.

GENTLEMAN: Your fortune, friend? (*He laughs.*)

MARTIN: Yes, sir, so said the fellow in my dream. So I left my village of Mulbridge and came all this way to London, and I have stood here upon the bridge as I was told, and today is the fortieth day.

GENTLEMAN (*laughing*): Well, friend, you have made two sixpences this day, for I saw you myself. Is that not a fortune for a poor country fellow?

MARTIN: Tell me, sir, if you will, do you think I shall make my fortune?

GENTLEMAN: Why, fellow, I will tell you what I think. I think you are foolish to trust in dreams and to wear yourself out in traveling these many miles for such foolishness. Get back to your village, and never believe such nonsense again.

MARTIN: In truth, sir, I did not think——

GENTLEMAN: Now, listen to me, you singer of foolish songs and peddler of silver pins that are not silver, I tell you what: do you suppose I would be such a fool as to trust in idle dreams? Why, I myself had a dream last night that if I were to go to a village in the country far away and dig below a walnut tree behind a peddler's cottage, I too should make my fortune. Do you think I should waste my time with such foolishness?

MARTIN: Do you say a walnut tree, sir? Behind a peddler's cottage——

GENTLEMAN: Why, what of that, fellow?

MARTIN: Why, sir, I thank you. I will go back straightway, for this is wonderful news you have given me. Here are three ribbons, sir, for your sweetheart and a cambric handkerchief for when you have a cold in the nose.

GENTLEMAN (*taking the ribbons and the handkerchief in incredulous amusement*): Now I see you are indeed a madman. I will go and tell my wife what a simple fellow I have met. Good-by fellow, and here is sixpence for your companion.

He tosses sixpence to the OLD MAN *and goes out.*

MARTIN: Good-by, sir. Did you hear what he said, old man? Now I will not wait till tomorrow but go home this minute.

OLD MAN: Did you say you were going back to the village of Mulbridge near Mulcaster?

MARTIN: Yes. It's there I live.

OLD MAN: May I go with you, peddler, for 'twas in Mulbridge I lived these many years past, before I set out for London to make my fortune. I am an old man and I would like to see my own village again before I die.

MARTIN: Do you know Mulbridge, old fellow? Well, come along with me. We will travel together and 'twill be a shorter journey for your company, al-

though you are an old man who can go but slowly.
Come.

MARTIN *has strapped up his pack. The* OLD MAN
has got to his feet and taking his stick and his beg-
ging cup he follows MARTIN.

As we go, I will tell you all that has happened in
the village since you went away to make your fortune.

ACT 3

The same as Act 1, about a week later. MARGERY *is*
sitting at the table doing some mending by the last
rays of the May sun. Enter GILLIAN *carrying a small*
chicken prepared for the pot.

GILLIAN: Look what Simon has sent us, mother—a
  spring chicken all ready for cooking.
MARGERY: The boy is foolish, giving you presents, for
  you will never marry him.
GILLIAN: Of course I shall marry him, just as soon as
  father comes home with money for the wedding.
MARGERY: Then you will die an old maid. Father will
  never come home. He has been gone nearly sixty
  days now. Why did I ever let him go?
GILLIAN: Well, we did not expect him back till now.

MARGERY: No, child, I was a fool to let him go.

GILLIAN: 'Tis too late to say that now, mother. Besides, as you said yourself, if you had not let him go he would never have ceased to fret and worry.

MARGERY: Yes, 'tis true. I should never have married a foolish man in the first place.

GILLIAN: He will come home any moment now, mother. You shall see. I have a feeling we shall see him sitting in his old place before you can say "needle."

MARGERY: Well, I will work no more with the needle now for it's nearly sundown. I have been mending his old coat against the time he comes, for if he does come, it's certain his clothes will be all in rags. He will not come tonight, that's plain.

GILLIAN (*taking the mending from her mother and laying it on one side*): You are tired, mother. Go and lie down, and I will put on the chicken for supper. When you are rested, 'twill be done.

MARGERY: Yes, the chicken. I do not like you taking chickens from Simon, Jill. It's not right.

GILLIAN: Never you mind that. The chicken was not for me but for you. Simon knows you are tired and lack food. Now you go and lie down.

MARGERY: Very well. (*Getting up and going to inner door.*) But why eat the fowl tonight? It will serve for dinner tomorrow.

GILLIAN: Maybe we shall need it for supper tonight. Maybe there will be company.

MARGERY: Your father will not come home, Jill, no more than my father will. The highwaymen have had him upon the roads or maybe he has perished of crocodiles on the Goodwin Sands——

GILLIAN: Nonsense, mother. Go to bed. Have we a bit of garlic to put in the pot with the chicken?

MARGERY: No, we have no garlic, for the new bed I planted under the walnut tree is not grown yet. I don't think it will ever grow, and all I shall have for my pains will be the ache in my bones.

GILLIAN: Well, I will go to neighbor Blackstone for some garlic. If I go across the fields I can be home again before it is dark.

MARGERY: Well, do as you please, but don't be long.

MARGERY *goes out.*

GILLIAN: I will be but a few minutes. The chicken will taste all the better for a piece of garlic.

GILLIAN *puts on a shawl and goes out. She does not pass the window. It is getting dark. Presently the sound of two voices is heard singing:*

> Fortune, fortune!
> Hear the bells of London Town,
> Silken hose and velvet gown.
> Fortune, fortune!
> Wheel go up and wheel come down.

MARTIN *and the* OLD MAN *appear at the window.*

They look in for a minute, then enter quietly.

MARTIN: Come in, father. Sit down and make yourself at home. Margery and the girl are both away from home, it seems.

He puts down his pack in a corner. The OLD MAN does not sit down but wanders round, looking at everything.

OLD MAN: Yes, Martin, this is the place. This is my brother's cottage that he left to me and my daughter Margery when he died. I remember it all after more than twenty years. So you are indeed my daughter's husband. Little did I think I should live to see this day.

MARTIN: Come, cheer up, old man. You are not attending your own funeral. Now see here. I will go and see if Margery is in and I will warn her that you have come back, for perhaps the shock of seeing you may upset her. Take this jug and these four pence (*gives him jug and money*) and go to Dame Crabtree's house on the high road by the end of the lane, and bring back a jug of her best cider. Are you strong enough to go? It's but a few steps.

OLD MAN: Ay, son, I will go as fast as I can.

OLD MAN goes out with the jug. Enter from the other door MARGERY, carrying a light, which she puts down on the table.

MARGERY: Why, Martin, it's you at last. (*They embrace each other.*) How foolish I was to think I should never see you again.

MARTIN: Why, Margery, my dear, did you think you could be rid of me so easy? Now tell me what is for supper, for I have made my fortune and I am hungry.

MARGERY: No, tell me what you have been doing? But was there not somebody with you? I was lying down for a while and I thought I heard voices. Have you begun talking to yourself?

MARTIN: Sit down, wife, for I have something to tell you. There is indeed another with me and it is someone you should know well. He has gone to get us some cider and will be here at once.

MARGERY: Who is it, Martin? Is it some rich fellow from London, maybe, or——

MARTIN: Yes, he is from London, but he is not a rich fellow. He is your own father, and he has become a beggar.

MARGERY: My father, did you say my father? No, husband, you have lost your wits and do mock me.

MARTIN: You shall see him for yourself—and right now, for here he comes.

OLD MAN *passes window, carrying jug carefully.* MARTIN *opens door, takes jug as* OLD MAN *comes in and stands holding it.*

Here is your father, Margery, and here is your own daughter, old man.

MARGERY: My father! Yes, it is he.

OLD MAN: Margery, my girl. (*They embrace one another.*)

MARTIN: Well, I will leave you two together like the loving couple in the ballad, and go and get my spade. (*He puts down the jug.*) I have work to do.

MARGERY: No, husband, you cannot go and dig by night. Are you quite mad?

MARTIN: I must to the walnut tree. There is a little daylight left—just so much daylight as I have wits! So don't delay me.

MARTIN *has gone out.*

MARGERY: Now sit down, father, and drink some cider. Tell me what you have done these many years. (*She pours cider for him. He drinks.*) And how did you come to meet my husband in London, and what is this nonsense of his about a fortune?

Before she has finished, GILLIAN *has come in.*

Why, Gillian, my dear, come in and greet your grandfather, my own father whom you have never seen. Father, here is our one child, our daughter Jill.

GILLIAN: My grandfather?

OLD MAN: I am glad to see you, my granddaughter. I might have known you for my daughter's child, for you are just like she was twenty years ago.

GILLIAN: I am glad to see you, sir, if indeed you are my grandfather, as mother says. But where is my father? Didn't you come with him?

MARGERY: Yes, child, your father is here and——

GILLIAN: Oh where is he? I knew he would come!

MARGERY: Your father is digging under the walnut tree. Alas, he is as mad as Tom O'Bedlam. It's lucky you have a mother with a head on her, for your father is——

GILLIAN: Look, there he is, under the walnut tree.

They all look out of the window excitedly. It is quite dark outside.

He is digging like a madman!

MARGERY: The great simpleton! He is digging up my new garlic bed that gave me the backache like——

OLD MAN: Has he found anything?

GILLIAN: He has stopped digging and thrown down his spade.

MARGERY: He is stooping to the ground!

GILLIAN: He has dug something up! It's—I cannot see what it is. Yes, it's a box! He is bringing it to the house. Father!

She rushes to the door, opens it and embraces MARTIN, who comes to the table, puts down a small, dirty box. All gather round.

MARTIN: Gillian, my lamb, it's good to see you——

GILLIAN: Oh, father, father, welcome home. What is this about your fortune? What is that dirty box?

MARTIN *is prying open the lid.*

MARGERY: Take it off my clean table, and tell me why you dug up my new garlic bed!

MARTIN: The devil take your garlic bed, my love, for here are better things than herbs.

MARTIN *holds up coins and silver objects triumphantly. All press round and handle the treasure. They gasp with astonishment, and all speak together.*

MARGERY: Let me see, let me see! It's real silver.

GILLIAN: These are gold coins.

OLD MAN: What have you there? All the treasures of Egypt?

MARTIN: Now did not I say I would find my fortune?

OLD MAN: Let me see. (*They stand back a little and fall silent as he speaks.*) Yes, these were my brother's things. Here are his silver plates, and here are the ornaments your mother had when she married, daughter. It was thought that he had riches, but none knew where he had hidden them. There were thieves in the countryside before he died, and he must have stowed them under the walnut tree for safety.

MARTIN: And there they would have lain till doomsday, had I not dreamed my dream, wife. Now you may have all the clothes you desire, Gillian, and marry Simon as soon as he will have you.

MARGERY: And I shall have a new henhouse, and you shall have a new coat, Martin, and father shall sit by the fire and drink the best cider. But I am faint with hunger. Put on the supper, child, and let us eat.

MARTIN: Yes, let us have supper and I will tell you all our adventures. (*Pouring out cider*.) And while supper is cooking, let us all have a drink of good cider, and sing the song of Golden Hair. (*The mugs are handed round. All join in singing and drinking as the curtain falls.*)

> As I do walk now here, now there
> With hey, the bonny eglantine.
> To take the wholesome country air,
> With hey, the bonny eglantine.
> My feet they wander everywhere,
> But my heart goes not with me,
> For see my love, it stays with thee,
> Golden Hair, Golden Hair,
> Tangled in thy golden hair.
> And, hey, the eglantine is bonny.

CURTAIN

MULCASTER MARKET

A Play in Four Acts Based on an Indian Story

✦ ✦ ✦

The Players

BLOCKHEAD ⎫
BAREBONES ⎬ Three Rogues
LONGLEGS ⎭
A LABORER

✦ ✦

ACT I

A crossroads. A signpost in the center of the stage points to MULCASTER, MULBRIDGE, *and* LON-DON. *The signpost stands in a hole in the center of a mound; it can be replaced by a tree for Acts 2, 3 and 4. This scenery can be dispensed with, if necessary.*

Enter from opposite sides, BAREBONES, *a beggar with a black patch over one eye, and* BLOCKHEAD, *a tall, foolish beggar. He has an educated voice in spite of his stammer.* BAREBONES *puts his bundle down and sits with his back to the signpost, takes out a clay pipe and lights it.* BLOCKHEAD *is singing a song. As the song finishes, he sits down beside* BAREBONES.

BLOCKHEAD:

> The master steals the maiden's heart,
> The cuckoo steals the robin's nest.
>> Come forth, come forth, ye robbers all,
> A beggar's life is all the best.
>> A beggar's life, a beggar's life,
> A beggar's life is all the best!

I will sit down beside you, Brother Barebones, so that I may get a whiff of your p-pipe, for I have no tobacco of my own, and tobacco is hard to come by.

BAREBONES: Sit down and welcome, Brother Blockhead, so long as you sing no more of your foolish song.

BLOCKHEAD: I ask p-pardon for my poor singing, but in truth I think it is n-not such a foolish s-song.

BAREBONES: You are a beggar yourself, Brother Blockhead, so how can you sing that a beggar's life is all the best?

BLOCKHEAD: It is like your tobacco—not very good, but there is no better to be had. Let me s-sit a little nearer, that I may s-smell it more strongly. Ah!

BAREBONES: Tell me, Blockhead, were you always a devotee of the vagabond's trade? In other words, were you always a beggar?

A BEGGAR'S LIFE

The mas-ter steals the maid-en's heart, The Cuck-oo steals the

rob-in's nest. Come forth, come forth ye rob—bers all, A

beg-gar's life is all the best. A beg-gar's life, a

beg-gar's life, A beg-gar's life is all the best.

BLOCKHEAD: No. I have f-followed many trades. I c-come of a very good family—a very old family. My mother was a Windfall.

BAREBONES: My mother was a thief, the best of her trade between Newcastle and Portsmouth. She taught me no trade but thieving, and a poor trade it is.

BLOCKHEAD: It's not such a bad trade, Brother Barebones. We wander where we will, we w-work for no man, we listen to the birds in summer and watch the b-buttercups in the meadows.

BAREBONES: We can eat neither b-birds nor b-butter-cups. We need food like other men, and just now my stomach is in urgent need of sustenance—in other words, I am hungry. Have you anything to eat, brother?

BLOCKHEAD: No. But I have two legs to carry me to Mulcaster Market, and a voice to sing me a song on the way. (*He sings.*)

> A beggar's life, a beggar's life,
> A beggar's life——

BAREBONES: Pray, do not sing. Your two legs, though they be as lean as a scarecrow's, may be strong; but your voice is like the rusty hinges of a barnyard door. It will scare the birds from the treetops and turn the buttercups blue. Moreover, you are a fool-ish man, and your idle talk stops me from thinking.

BLOCKHEAD: You may be w-wiser than I, Brother Barebones, but you have had no more to eat this week than I have. W-what are you thinking of?

BAREBONES: Food, brother. Food and drink. What else is there to think of?

BLOCKHEAD: Money, brother. Rich farmers who might be coming this way from Mulcaster Market, with their stomachs full of food and their b-bags full of silver.

BAREBONES: Never a penny will they give you and me. For nowadays they are all as mean and miserly as a skeleton in Mulcaster graveyard. And it is in the graveyard that all beggars will soon be lying, if they have no more to eat than I have had this year. What could I not give for a dish of fat ham and three fried eggs and a quart of cider at the King's Head by Mulcaster jail!

BLOCKHEAD: What have you to give, Brother Bare-bones, but the black patch over your eye and your little tobacco-pipe? But don't t-talk to me of M-mulcaster jail, for I spent fourteen days there once, and it is a place I like the outside of better than the inside.

BAREBONES: I tell you what, Brother. If I had the chance of robbing a rich farmer of two fat hens and a string of pork sausages, I would spend a month in Mulcaster jail and live on dry bread and rusty water. But here comes another of our trade.

Enter LONGLEGS, *a skinny old beggar with only one leg and a pair of crutches. He hobbles in excitedly.*

LONGLEGS: News, brothers! I have news. If your ears are as hungry as your stomachs, stop your idle tongues and listen to me.

BAREBONES: What news can you tell, Sir Longlegs? Has the mayor invited us all to dinner with the aldermen and their wives?

LONGLEGS: You are foolish, Master Barebones. When you were lying in your cradle thinking how to pick your father's pocket, I was walking the roads learning how to wheedle sixpence out of a poor widow woman! But let me take the weight off my one leg, and you shall hear what I have to tell.

LONGLEGS *sits between the others.*

BAREBONES: Speak on, ancient one. Let your story be short or you will drop into your grave before it is done.

LONGLEGS: If I were to hit you over the head with my crutch, Barebones, your head would break my crutch in two pieces, and therefore I will not do it. But if I were a dozen years younger . . .

BLOCKHEAD: I pray you, brothers, stop quarreling and l-let us hear the t-tale.

LONGLEGS: Listen to me, then. Yonder is coming up the road from Mulcaster a fellow who has bought in the market a great fat side of bacon. Did I not hear you talk of robbing? Let us think of a way of robbing this fellow and getting the bacon for ourselves.

BAREBONES: A likely story, you grandfather of all liars! How did you, with your one leg and your seventy-seven years, pass this husky fellow on the Mulcaster road?

LONGLEGS: I did not pass him, brother college professor with the bulging brain. I saw him sitting inside the King's Head at Mulcaster with his side of bacon laid on his knees like a sleeping baby—so peaceful, so quiet, so rosy it was. "Aha," thought I——

BAREBONES: Why did you not beg it from him, you who can beg crown pieces from poor widows? Answer me that.

BLOCKHEAD: Brothers, brothers, let us not quarrel. Let us think how we may get this b-bacon for ourselves. A dish of bacon is as fair a sight to me as a tree full of b-birds or a field full of b-buttercups.

BAREBONES: What were you doing at the King's Head in Mulcaster, Sir Longlegs?

LONGLEGS: I was passing the door. As I passed, I saw this fellow with the bacon talking with his neighbor. Come closer and I will tell you what he said.

They move closer.

LONGLEGS: I heard this fellow with the bacon say that he would be going home along the Mulbridge Road and that he would be alone. I stayed to hear no more, but came on to tell you, as fast as my three legs would bring me.

BLOCKHEAD: Why then, we may knock him down and run off with his bacon. It will be no more difficult than picking daisies.

LONGLEGS: No. For this fellow is a husky laborer, a ploughman I should guess. He looks strong enough to be a blacksmith. Will *you* strike him first, Master Blockhead?

BLOCKHEAD: No.

LONGLEGS: Nor I. How about Brother Barebones?

BAREBONES: Robbery with violence is a foolish way. It will only land us all in Mulcaster jail.

BLOCKHEAD: Didn't you say you would willingly go to jail for a meal of bacon and fried eggs, Brother?

BAREBONES: Not when I may get it otherwise. I think I see how we may get this fat bacon by trickery. Tell me, Father, did this laboring fellow see you?

LONGLEGS: No. For I heard him through the open window, and for the most part his face was hidden in his mug of cider.

BAREBONES: Very well, then. I know what to do. Come, let me help you to your feet. (*He helps* LONGLEGS *up.*)

BLOCKHEAD: W-what shall we do, Brother Barebones?

BAREBONES: Let your mind dwell upon buttercups and your tongue resemble the clapper of a bell that has lost its rope—in other words, shut up! Come with me a little way along the road, where there are three trees at a short distance from each other. And as we go, I shall tell you what we must do. Now under the first of these trees, Blockhead, you shall sit——

They go out.

ACT 2

*The roadside. In the center of the stage is a tree.
Enter the Three Beggars.*

BAREBONES: Here is the place. You sit down here,
Blockhead, and do not go to sleep. When this fellow
comes, do exactly as I have said. When he has gone,
wait a little while and follow behind.

BLOCKHEAD: Very good, Brother Barebones. I will not
fall asleep—or if I do, it will be with dreaming of
buttercups and daisies.

LONGLEGS: Better think about bacon. But here comes
the fellow! I know him by his clothes; and see! yes,
he has the bacon over his back. Come along, Barebones. There is no time to lose.

BAREBONES: Come, I will take you to the next tree.

(*Going.*)

BLOCKHEAD: Shall I sing, to keep up my spirits?

BAREBONES: Sing if you must! But do not scare away
the laboring fellow!

BAREBONES *and* LONGLEGS *go out.*

BLOCKHEAD (*singing*):

The master steals the maiden's heart,
The cuckoo steals the robin's nest.
Come forth, come forth, ye robbers all——

Enter LABORER *with a side of bacon. He is a tall, strong fellow, well-fed and prosperous, although not clever.*

LABORER: Good day, fellow.

BLOCKHEAD: Good day, ploughman. 'Tis a hot day. Will you not sit down with me under this s-sycamore tree and listen to the b-birds awhile?

LABORER: Ay, the weather is warm, and I have a way to go. I will sit down with you. Did I not hear you singing a song about robbers?

BLOCKHEAD: Robbers? Why no, sir. What should I know about robbers? Are there robbers about here?

LABORER: I hope not, fellow. For I have here a side of bacon that I bought in Mulcaster Market.

BLOCKHEAD: A side of bacon, sir?

LABORER: Yes, here it is. It cost me all I had.

BLOCKHEAD: Let me see it. Why I hope, sir, you did not give much for it.

LABORER: Don't you think it's worth much?

BLOCKHEAD: Well, perhaps it's not so bad. I tell you what. I picked a basket of gooseberries yesterday in my garden, and if I had not eaten the greater part of them last night, I would give you the gooseberries in exchange for the bacon—just to oblige an honest t-traveler.

LABORER (*rising indignantly*): A basket of gooseberries! Why, fellow, I gave good honest silver for this side of bacon.

BLOCKHEAD: Did you indeed? But see how stingy and thin it is, neighbor!

LABORER: The farmer I bought it off said 'twas right fat—corn-fed, he said his hogs were.

BLOCKHEAD: Corn-fed? Oh no, sir, p-pardon me. The worthy farmer must have been speaking in jest.

LABORER (*rises*): I must be off home, sir. I am sorry you think so ill of my bargain. Maybe you are mistaken.

BLOCKHEAD: Ay, take your bacon home, for the day is hot, and ere long 'twill all melt away. Can you spare a penny, friend, to buy me a little mug of cider at the next inn?

LABORER: Your advice is worth no penny to me, fellow. Besides, I have given my all for the bacon, and have nothing left.

BLOCKHEAD: Well, tell that not to your wife, for I warrant she knows a scraggy bit of bacon when she sees it, even if you do not. Good-by, neighbor!

LABORER *goes off.*

ACT 3

The roadside. A tree, center. LONGLEGS *is sitting under it.*

LONGLEGS: Here I will sit under this chestnut tree till

my honest ploughman comes by. Ah! I hear him.
He walks slowly. Perhaps Brother Blockhead has
given him something to think about. Blockhead is a
foolish fellow, but he is not so simple as this fellow
with the bacon.

LABORER *comes in.*

Good day, sir. I am an old man, sir, and I can work
no more. Can you give me a penny to help me buy
a crust of bread?

LABORER: Alas, old fellow, I have not a copper to
spare.

LONGLEGS: Why, then, sit down and tell me how you
came to lose your money.

LABORER *sits.*

LABORER: It is a hot day and I will sit with you for a
while under this chestnut tree.

LONGLEGS: It is a sad thing to have no work, sir. I was
once hale and hearty like you, and had a good trade.

LABORER: And what was your trade?

LONGLEGS: In truth, sir, I was a pork butcher in
Mulcaster. But an accident lost me one of my legs
and I am now forced to beg.

LABORER: A pork butcher. Did you say a pork
butcher?

LONGLEGS: Ay, sir. A pork butcher. What of that?
But you look troubled. Will you not tell me what is
on your mind?

LABORER: Well, old man, it is like this. Did you say you had been a pork butcher?

LONGLEGS: Yes, indeed. But I lost my trade through a broken leg—that and dishonest farmers.

LABORER: Dishonest farmers?

LONGLEGS: Ay, sir. There are many dishonest farmers in these parts—especially in the pig trade.

LABORER: Specially in the pig trade? Oh dear, oh dear. Tell me, my honest friend, can you tell a good side of bacon when you see it?

LONGLEGS: Yes, sir. But I have not seen a good one these ten years.

LABORER: I have here a side of bacon that I bought in Mulcaster Market.

LONGLEGS: Let me see it, I pray you.

LABORER: Why, here it is. Now tell me, is that not a good honest piece of bacon?

LONGLEGS: 'Tis an honest piece of bacon, sir. The bacon is honest, but I fear the fellow that sold it to you might not have been so honest. Still, you did not give much for it?

LABORER: I gave all I had. It is good fat bacon, and the weight of it is very great. It's all I can do to carry it home.

LONGLEGS: This is not fat, my friend, 'tis all bone.

LABORER: A rude fellow I met with just now offered me a basket of gooseberries for it.

LONGLEGS: Ha ha! A basket of gooseberries! That's a good joke, that. But he was a rude fellow indeed.

It's worth more than that. It's worth a bushel of potatoes—ay, perhaps two bushels, though not of the best sort.

LABORER: Well, whether it be good or bad I must get it home. But when I meet with that farmer again, I shall have something to tell him. (*He gets up to go.*)

LONGLEGS: Ay, sir. There are many dishonest, swindling fellows in this country. They are too clever for simple folks like you and me. They lost me my trade, curse them! I wish I had met you to warn you against them sooner. It's a shame, honest fellow!

LABORER: Good day, old fellow. I must be going, for I have far to go, and I do not know what my wife will say when I tell her I have met with robbers in Mulcaster Market.

LONGLEGS: Good day, sir. And may you meet with no more robbers this day!

LABORER *goes.*

A basket of gooseberries! Young Master Blockhead is not such a blockhead after all! But here he comes. I must wait for him here, and we will follow after our simple friend. Well done, Master Blockhead!

(*He gets to his feet.*)

ACT 4

The roadside. Tree, center. BAREBONES *is looking down the road towards Mulcaster.*

BAREBONES: Here he comes. He looks tired and dejected. What a fine fat ham he bears on his shoulder. Ah! I can almost smell it from here. Let me be sleeping under this shady elm tree.

    BAREBONES *lies down and snores gently. Enter* LABORER.

LABORER: Dear me, dear me! How hot it is! What will my wife say when she sees me with this miserable piece of salt pork? A dear woman, my wife, but alas! not too gentle with her tongue. What? Another beggar! Poor fellow, how tired he looks. I had not better wake him.

    BAREBONES *wakes and sits up.*

BAREBONES: A thousand curses! Ten thousand curses! Who are you, clumsy rogue, who interferes with the noonday slumbers of an innocent tramp—in other words, why the devil did you wake me up?

LABORER: Oh sir, pardon me. I saw you were asleep and tried to tread softly, but I fear I am a clumsy fellow and can not walk quietly in my ploughman's boots.

BAREBONES: It was not your boots that woke me, fellow, but the stink of your dog.

LABORER: Dog, sir? I have no dog.

BAREBONES: Is not that a dead dog you are carrying on your shoulder? Poo! Take it away. It has a most nauseating odor. It smells like the stable yard that has not been cleaned out, like a pond in summer that is covered with green slime, like—

LABORER: Is it as bad as that, sir? It has been called scraggy, it is said to be full of bones, but you are the first to say that it smells.

BAREBONES: No doubt it was a good dog, a faithful dog, a wonderful catcher of rats and frightener of thieves. But, fellow, it is now a very smelly dog, and I pray you, take it away!

LABORER: It is not a dog at all, sir. It is a side of bacon.

BAREBONES: Bacon? Bacon? Would you make fun of me?

LABORER: Why, no, sir. On my honor——

BAREBONES: I have but one eye and am half blind. But surely I know a dead dog when I see one. Bring it closer that I may look at it. I will hold my nose. (*He inspects the bacon.*) Poo! Stand further off. Yes, indeed, it was bacon once. But who has played you this scurvy trick and sold you a decayed piece of pork fit only to be made into shoe leather?

LABORER: A farmer it was, sir, in Mulcaster Market.

BAREBONES: One farmer Giles, was it?

LABORER: No, sir. 'Twas Farmer Hodge that sold me the bacon. I gave him good silver for it—all that I had saved in three months.

BAREBONES (*in horror, stepping back*): Farmer Hodge! Did you say Farmer Hodge, fellow?

LABORER: Ay, sir, 'twas Farmer Hodge that——

BAREBONES: But have you not heard, simpleton? Why, all the countryside knows that a week or ten days ago all Farmer Hodge's pigs—ay and his sheep and cows too, and the rooster that crowed on his barnyard roof—all his animals were smitten with a horrible disease and instantly died of it.

LABORER: What disease?

BAREBONES: A disease called crypto-concoid syphonostimata—in other words, scarlet fever. It's a terrible plague! You had best throw away the carcase instantly, or it will give you the fever and you will die, and all your hens and rabbits too—ay, and even your wife and little children. It is a terrible disaster, this crypto-concoid syphonostimata. Indeed I am sorry for you, my poor fellow.

LABORER (*throwing down the bacon in disgust*): A curse upon all dishonest, swindling farmers! I have given all the money I have for a rotten piece of bacon and carried it halfway home in the heat of the day, and perhaps got the red fever into the bargain. I thank you for telling me this, honest friend. I will go home and tell my wife you saved her life and mine, and the lives of our children and our hens and rabbits too.

BAREBONES: Do not thank me, fellow. I will bury this wretched piece of bacon for you, so that it does not spread disease through all the country, and tomorrow I will inform the magistrates against Farmer Hodge. Good day, my friend, and may you never be swindled again as you have been swindled this day.

LABORER: Here is a packet of tobacco for you, that I bought in Mulcaster Market. Put it in your pipe to drive away the smell of this carcase. Here. (*Gives* BAREBONES *tobacco.*)

BAREBONES: I like not to take this, but as you say, it will help me to bear the smell of the bacon while I bury it in the ground. Good-by to you.

LABORER: Good day to you, sir. Would that all men were as honest as you.

LABORER *goes.* BLOCKHEAD *and* LONGLEGS *are heard singing.* BAREBONES *picks up the bacon, sits down and smells it with relish. He takes tobacco and begins filling his pipe. The others come in singing.*

BLOCKHEAD *and* LONGLEGS·

Come forth, come forth, ye robbers all,
A beggar's life is all the best.

A beggar's life, a beggar's life,
A beggar's life is all the best.

LONGLEGS: Has the laboring fellow gone home to his wife? And have you the bacon, Barebones?

BAREBONES: Ay, here it is. See here!

LONGLEGS *and* BLOCKHEAD (*together*): Hooray! Hooray! A beggar's life is all the best!

BLOCKHEAD: Let me see it. (*Takes bacon from* BAREBONES): Ah! It smells good. It is tender and fat, it is well seasoned and would feast a man for a week. And I offered him a basket of gooseberries for it!

BAREBONES: No, 'twas me that got it away from him by saying it was from a pig that had died of the red fever.

LONGLEGS: No, you lying rogue, 'twas I that told him it was scraggy and full of bone——

BAREBONES: No, you lying old grandfather——

LONGLEGS: Yes, and 'twas no good but for making shoe leather, I told him——

BLOCKHEAD: Father Longlegs, do not boast——

LONGLEGS: Go to the devil, you fool. 'Twas I that——

BAREBONES: Boast not so loud, you miserable old——

BLOCKHEAD: No, do not quarrel, masters. Let us go taste this b-beautiful b-bacon. I know a place down by the river where we may listen to the birds and watch the b-buttercups——

Neither of the others take any notice of him, but

they go on quarreling while he says the above lines, so with his last words BLOCKHEAD *steals out, taking the bacon with him and singing his song.*

LONGLEGS: Now I tell you, you miserable, one-eyed son of a pickpocket, it was I that first got a sight of the bacon, was it not?

BAREBONES: And who was it that thought of the way of stealing it?

LONGLEGS: Why, you bragging whippersnapper——

BAREBONES: Hey, Longlegs, you doddering skeleton, where is the bacon?

LONGLEGS: And where is Blockhead, the pilfering knave? After him, after him! We have been robbed!

BAREBONES *rushes out crying* "Stop, thief! Stop, you rogue!" LONGLEGS *hurries after him.*

CURTAIN

THE STOLEN BOY

✦   ✦   ✦

The Players

JOHN CATCHPOLE, a shopkeeper
BARNEY, his servant
THE STRANGER
KATE CATCHPOLE, the shopkeeper's wife
ROBIN, the shopkeeper's son
A TRAVELER
A CONSTABLE OF THE WATCH

✦   ✦

ACT I

A roadside. Summer evening. A rough bench with a hedge or clump of bushes behind it. The weather is hot and thundery. There is a distant rumble of thunder and the STRANGER appears. He runs in furtively, looks round as if afraid of pursuers and then hides quickly in some convenient place—if there is a hedge or bush behind the bench, he hides there. He has a dark, sullen face and a black beard, a black cloak with a hood and a traveler's wallet or satchel.

Enter JOHN CATCHPOLE, *an elderly shopkeeper, decently but poorly dressed. He is tired and limps along with the aid of a stick. He is crusty but not ill-natured. He is followed by his servant* BARNEY, *a cheerful, foolish young man, carrying an enormous pack over his back.*

JOHN: I can go no further, Barney. Let us sit down for a few minutes on the bench here. (*He hobbles to bench and sits down.*) Be careful how you put down that pack.

BARNEY (*lowering the pack gingerly to the ground and sitting down*): Tell me, master, why did you choose the hottest day in summer to go to the fair and buy this pack full of pots and dishes?

JOHN: I did not choose it, simpleton. Besides, I did not know it would be hot.

BARNEY: Nor did you know that you would sprain your ankle upon a loose stone. Tell me, master, why did you sprain your ankle?

JOHN (*crossly*): Because I like sitting here in the sun talking to a simpleton!

BARNEY: Why, so do I, too. What shall we talk about?

There is a rather louder rumble of thunder.

Oh, master, did you hear the rumble of lightning? Will it strike us, think you?

JOHN: Yes, very likely. For it is the devil himself come to summon us both to hell—you for being an idiot and me for giving you protection. Listen, idiot——

BARNEY: Oh master, I am scared of your master the devil. What shall I do?

JOHN: Listen to me. I must stay here for a while till my foot mends. Perhaps a cart will come by that will carry me. If not, I will follow as best I can. You must hurry on to Mulcaster and warn your mistress that I am not badly hurt. Otherwise she will be anxious.

BARNEY (*cheerfully, as always*): Yes, she is a worrying anxious body, is Mistress Kate. Why did a clever fellow like you marry her, master?

JOHN: That's nothing to you. Now——

BARNEY: Well, you have a fine child. I hope the devil and his thunderstorm will not hurt Master Robin.

Thunder.

Oh, heaven have mercy upon us! Please, master devil——

He goes down on his knees. JOHN *prods him to his feet with his stick.*

JOHN: Be off, you idle fellow! Go by the highroad for there are thieves and rogues in every lane.

BARNEY: Yes, master,

JOHN: Do not stop to talk to anyone, and be careful with my dishes.

BARNEY: Yes, master,

JOHN: When you get to Mulcaster, go straight home

and put down the dishes carefully in the shop.

BARNEY: Yes, master.

JOHN: Tell your mistress that I have hurt my foot and will follow as fast as I may.

BARNEY: Yes, master. But, sir——

JOHN: Well, what is it?

BARNEY: Would it not be best for you to go home first and tell her yourself, for perhaps I will not remember.

JOHN: Why, you simpleton, you dolt and brother to a toadstool, how can I go first with my sprained ankle?

BARNEY: Oh, I had forgot your ankle. Never fear, master John, I will do all you say. (*He begins to go, then turns back.*) But master——

JOHN: Well, what is it now?

BARNEY: What if I be struck down by lightning and blasted by thunder?

JOHN (*rising painfully and limping toward him with his stick raised*): Prattle no more, you turnip-headed——

BARNEY: Yes, sir, I fly.

    As JOHN *chases him out, there is a terrific clap of thunder accompanied by lightning. Unseen to* JOHN, *the* STRANGER *appears from behind the hedge and sits down on the bench.*

JOHN: Why was I ever plagued with such an idiot for a servant? Oh, my foot, my foot!

(*He turns back to the bench and sees the* STRAN-
GER. *He stops short.*) Oh, pardon me, sir. I did not
see you. (*A pause. Then the* STRANGER *speaks. He
has a slow, rather rough, but grave voice.*)

STRANGER: Sit down. Do not be afraid. (*A pause.*)
Come, sit down beside me.

JOHN: Who are you, sir?

STRANGER: Maybe—maybe I am the devil. (*Distant
thunder.* JOHN *looks round fearfully.*)

STRANGER: No, do not turn to fly. Your sprained ankle
will not let you get far. I will not harm you. Come
and sit down at my side.

JOHN *goes slowly to the bench and sits down as
far as he can get from the* STRANGER.

STRANGER: Now tell me who you are. Perhaps I can
help you.

JOHN: No, I want no help——

STRANGER: What is your name?

JOHN: John Catchpole.

STRANGER: Your wife?

JOHN: Catherine. But——

STRANGER: You have a son?

JOHN: Yes, a boy. But I——

STRANGER: How old is your boy Robin?

Thunder.

JOHN: Seven. Now listen to me: I do not know if you

are the devil or not, but I will have nothing to do with you! (*He gets up and totters.*)

STRANGER (*rising and pulling* JOHN *back on to the bench as he speaks*): Do not go. I am a poor traveler and it is ill manners to treat me in this way. Listen. You are a shopkeeper in Mulcaster city and you are poor. You must be poor or you would not have to fetch your wares on foot. Poor men have need of help. Perhaps I can help you. Come, times are hard, are they not?

JOHN: Yes, sir. They are always hard for poor shop-keepers. I shall never make my fortune selling earthenware pots and dishes to other people.

STRANGER: You need a horse and cart. You need good clothes for yourself and your wife. You need food for your child. (*Thunder.*) Later you will need books and schoolmasters.

JOHN: Yes, but——

STRANGER: I will help you, master Catchpole.

JOHN: How can *you* help me? You said you were poor.

STRANGER: Where is your shop?

JOHN: In Bullfinch Lane, next to the sign of the Plough.

STRANGER: I will come and see you there, and poor as I am, I will do all I can to help you. But you must give me the most precious thing in your whole shop.

JOHN: Why, gladly will I. For my wares are poor, and there is not much that is of value. But what will you give me for it?

STRANGER: You shall see. Ask me not. Now, get on your way. Does your ankle feel better now?

JOHN *gets up and hobbles about a little more easily.*

JOHN: Yes, it is a little easier. Well, I am grateful to you, stranger. I am glad of your talk, whether I see you again or not.

STRANGER: I shall come, never fear.

JOHN: I am a poor man, and have many cares. People have little money now, and that makes them careful, so that they do not break dishes as they used to in better times. I would certainly not be sorry to have more money to spend.

STRANGER: One thing, master Catchpole.

JOHN: Yes?

STRANGER: Tell no one of your talk with me. Tell none that you have seen me, not even your wife.

JOHN: I will tell no one, if you say so—no one at all.

Thunder.

STRANGER: Now get you home, and farewell.

JOHN: Good-by, sir. (*Going.*) You have not told me your name.

STRANGER: I have told you who I am. My friends call me—Nick.

There is a loud clap of thunder.

JOHN (*as he goes*): Good-by—Nick!

The STRANGER *has once more disappeared behind the hedge.*

ACT 2

The same evening. It is almost dark. Inside JOHN CATCHPOLE's *shop in Mulcaster. There is a door leading inside the house, and another into the street. There is a table with two chairs beside it. A mattress in one corner. Shelves with earthenware dishes, mugs, etc. There is a lamp hanging from a bracket on the wall.* ROBIN, *aged seven, is sitting at a table. His mother,* KATE CATCHPOLE, *sets down a mug of milk, some bread and butter and an apple on the table. She is a kind-hearted but anxious, fretful woman of between 35 and 40.*

KATE: Make haste and eat your supper, Robin. It's late and you will catch cold sitting there in your night clothes.

ROBIN: Will father come and say good night to me?

KATE: Yes, when he has rested his foot.

ROBIN: How did father hurt his foot, mother?

KATE: I don't know. Get on with your supper. You'll never grow a big strong boy if you don't get enough sleep.

ROBIN: All right, mother. Can Barney come and say good night too?

KATE: Yes, yes. You know he always does.

There is a sound of wind and rain. The shutters outside the window flap. KATE takes up some mending and sits beside ROBIN as he continues his supper.

ROBIN: I like Barney. He plays with me and asks me riddles.

KATE: Barney is a child like you, boy. A foolish child, too. He causes your father a deal of trouble.

ROBIN: If I had a brother or sister, I could play with them. Why haven't I a brother or sister, mother?

KATE: Never you mind. One child is enough for poor people like us at our time of life. Have you drunk all your milk?

ROBIN: Nearly. But if I had a brother, I would not want to play with Barney. Barney is a sort of brother to me, isn't he?

KATE (*rising and going to inner door*): Heaven forbid! (*calling*) Barney!

ROBIN: Hark at the wind and rain! Why——

KATE: Barney, come here! Finish your supper, child. You'll be so tired in the morning.

ROBIN: Why am I going to sleep in here, mother?

KATE: Because the rain has come in through the attic roof and I am afraid you will catch cold.

BARNEY comes in with a pile of dishes which he puts on a shelf.

ROBIN: Will Barney be sleeping here too?

KATE: Barney! Oh, there you are. No, Barney will stay in the attic. He is stronger than you.

BARNEY: A little water on the brain will not hurt me, master Robin.

KATE: Barney, will you go and fasten the shutter outside? The wind is banging it and it will keep the boy awake.

ROBIN: Barney, will you finish the story of the old woman and the pig?

JOHN (*calling from within*): Barney, come and carry some more of these dishes, will you?

BARNEY: Now, what am I to do? I have only three hands. You finish your supper, Robin, and when you are in bed I will tell you a story. (*He goes outside and fastens the shutters. Noise of wind and rain.*)

ROBIN (*cramming the last of the bread into his mouth, taking the apple and jumping on to the mattress*): Oh good, Barney will tell me a story! (KATE *pulls the covers over him, takes up the plate and mug and goes toward the inner door as* BARNEY *returns, shaking the rain off.*)

KATE: Now, don't keep him up long, Barney, and do not excite the boy with your ghost stories. (*She goes.*)

BARNEY (*sitting down at the table*): 'Tis a rainy night, Robin. The thunderstorm is still rumbling around.

ROBIN: I am not afraid of storms. What makes the thunder?

BARNEY: I know not. Your father says it is the devil himself in a bad temper.

JOHN's *voice*: Barney, I say!

ROBIN: Well I am not afraid of the devil.

BARNEY: And I am not afraid of your father. Come now, which story will you have?

ROBIN: The old woman and the pig.

BARNEY (*drawing chair closer to bed*): Well, there was once an old pig that was taking a woman to market. No, that's wrong. To tell the truth, master Robin, I have forgotten the story. I will ask you a riddle.

JOHN's *voice*: Barney!

BARNEY: Now listen carefully. Coming, master! When is a hen not an egg?

ROBIN: When is a hen——?

BARNEY: No, that's wrong. When is an egg——

JOHN *comes in with a paper in his hand.*

JOHN: Stop talking nonsense, you rascal, and attend to me. Where is that dozen of ladles you unpacked?

BARNEY: Over in the corner by the great bowls. But there are not a dozen, master.

JOHN: Not a dozen? Why not?

BARNEY: Because I have broken two of them, sir. It was when I tripped over the pile of mugs that stood in my way.

JOHN: Tripped over a pile of mugs? Then how many mugs did you break?

BARNEY: Not more than three, master. But if I had not been carrying the big pitchers with the——

JOHN: Pitchers? Pitchers? Do not tell me how many of them you have smashed, you great, clumsy, good-for-nothing——

Re-enter KATE.

KATE: For shame, John. Do not use such language before the boy.

JOHN: I have said nothing yet. Wait till I get started!

ROBIN: No, do not call Barney names in front of me, father. I love Barney. He is my brother, are you not, Barney?

JOHN: Merciful Heavens!

KATE: I pray you, John, and you too Barney, do not stand talking here all night and keeping the boy from his sleep. I have worked for him night and day for seven years and he is all I have and if he gets no sleep he will be a feeble, puny child fit for nothing at all.

JOHN: Yes, indeed, and I have heard this every night for as many years. But it is all very well for you to talk, my dear. You do not have to pay out your hard-earned silver to buy pots and dishes for this lumbering idiot to smash like a great oaf at a country fair. Five miles have I tramped this hot summer's day to bring back wares for my shop, and it is little you care whether we prosper or get flung out into the streets because we cannot pay the rent!

Well, now, let the lad get some sleep. Have you shut up the fowls, Barney?

BARNEY: Yes, master. I have let out the fowls and shut up the cat, washed the shutters and fastened the dishes and now, I will get me some supper and go to bed. Good night, Robin. If I think of the end of your story in the night, I will not wake you up to tell it to you.

BARNEY *goes*.

ROBIN: Good night, Barney, good night.

JOHN: Well, Kate, I am weary. Let us have a little supper and go to bed, for we must open the shop early in the morning.

KATE: I do not like this wind and rain, John. I am afraid the storm will come back. Do you think the boy will be safe?

JOHN: Ay, to be sure. You were ever a fretting, worrying woman, my dear. The boy has seen many a thunderstorm before now. You are not afraid, eh, Robin?

ROBIN: No, father, I like it here. It is warm and dry. But I feel hot. May I have some water?

KATE: Dear, oh dear! Perhaps the boy has a fever. Had I not better have him with me?

JOHN: Fiddle-faddle, woman! If you had your way, he should have a cold and a fever every other day of his life. Go and get him some water to put beside his bed and he will be asleep in five minutes.

KATE *goes out.*

JOHN: Good night, boy. Sleep soundly and may you sleep as well when you are as old as me. Did Barney say he had fastened everything up?

KATE *returns with a mug of water which she puts down beside* ROBIN's *bed.*

ROBIN: Yes, father. Good night.

JOHN: Good night, Robin. Come now, Kate. (*He goes and takes down the lamp from the wall.*)

KATE: There is the water, child. Good night and God bless you.

ROBIN: Thank you, mother. (*She kisses him and follows* JOHN *to the inner door.*)

KATE: Keep warm, Robin. Sleep well.

ROBIN: Never fear, mother.

He turns round to sleep. JOHN *follows* KATE *out, taking the lamp. The door closes. There is a flash of lightning, followed by thunder. Wind and rain louder. Then, after a few moments, a still louder clap of thunder accompanied by a vivid flash of lightning. The outer door flies in with a bang.* ROBIN *sits up in bed. The* STRANGER *appears at the door.*

ROBIN: Who's there? (*He seizes the mug of water at his side.*)

STRANGER: Who's there? Robin Catchpole?

ROBIN: Yes. Who are you?

STRANGER: The devil!

ROBIN: I am not afraid of the devil! (*He has scrambled out of bed and hurls the mug at the* STRANGER, *then retreats, but trips over a chair and sprawls across the table.*)

STRANGER (*rushing into the room and seizing him*): Come here, you villainous morsel of devil's food. Do you want me to eat you? Come with me. Your father has sold you to me!

ROBIN *screams as the* STRANGER *hauls him out of the shop.*

ROBIN: Let me go! Let me go!

As they go, there is another lightning flash, thunder, wind and rain. JOHN *rushes in from the inner door with the lamp, followed by* KATE *and* BARNEY.

KATE: What has happened?

BARNEY: The storm has broke in and——

JOHN: The boy! The boy has gone! Robin, where are you?

KATE (*who has rushed to the empty bed*): My boy, my boy! Where is he? Robin, Robin!

JOHN (*putting the lamp down on the table*): Somebody has been in and stolen the boy! Quick, Barney, follow him!

BARNEY (*stopping on the outer threshold and picking*

up a purse, which he throws down on the table):
Look, he has left something behind him. (*He runs
out into the street.*)

JOHN: It is some thief and he has dropped his purse.

KATE: Don't stand there, don't stand there! After him.

JOHN: I will call up the watch. Go, wife, and fetch the
neighbors. They will help us search for him.

BARNEY *returns.*

I thought you had locked up and made everything
fast.

BARNEY: The thief is nowhere to be seen. The street is
empty and there is no sign of them!

JOHN: Well, go next door and ask for help. I will see
if I can rouse the watchman. Help, help, thieves!

BARNEY: Thieves, thieves! They have stolen my master's child.

JOHN *and* BARNEY *are outside by now. Wind and
rain. The door slams shut.* KATE *is left alone; she
subsides to the table, weeping hysterically.*

KATE: Oh my boy, my little boy! I shall never see you
again, my little Robin. He was the most precious
thing in the house—the most precious thing in all the
house.

ACT 3

Scene I

*Ten years later. The roadside. Same scene as in
Act 1. The* STRANGER, *his beard and hair a little gray,
but still wearing a black cloak, runs in, pursued by*
ROBIN, *who strikes him with a cudgel, but not very
hard. At seventeen* ROBIN *is a well-grown boy, rather
rough of speech, dressed in poor clothing.*

STRANGER: Help, oh help me! Do not strike an old
man, you rogue!

ROBIN: Take that! Take that!

STRANGER: Give me back my purse, you young thief!

ROBIN: I need it more than you, you old miser!

STRANGER: No, I am a poor man! Give it back,
you——

ROBIN: Take that instead!

With a last blow, ROBIN *leaps on to the seat and
disappears behind the hedge. The* STRANGER *falls to
the ground, groaning and crying for help.*

STRANGER: Wait till the justices catch you, you young
blackguard! Help me, oh help me! I am robbed.

Enter a TRAVELER, *a well-dressed man of middle
age.*

TRAVELER: Which way did he go? I will follow him!

STRANGER: No, sir, stay and help me, I pray you. I was set upon and robbed. Two sturdy fellows—oh, help me. I am faint——

TRAVELER: Here, drink a little of this.

He gives the STRANGER *a drink from a flask.*

STRANGER: Thank'ee, sir. Ah, these villainous, thieving young rogues. The countryside is not safe for honest men.

TRAVELER: Have you strength to get to this bench now, if I help you?

He helps the STRANGER *to the bench, and stands beside him. As the* TRAVELER *lifts him up, he steals his purse.*

Tell me how this happened, old man?

STRANGER: Why, sir, as I was walking this road just now, two sturdy fellows sprang out of that hazel hedge and demanded my purse. One of them took it from me and the other cudgeled me with his stick. Didn't you see one of them run away?

TRAVELER: No, but I heard your cries. Which way did these ruffians go?

STRANGER: I did not see them. I must get me to town and tell the magistrates.

TRAVELER: I am sorry you are hurt. I am sorry you are robbed too. Here, let me give you a little money to help you——

STRANGER (*hastily*): No, no, sir. I want no money. I

am a poor man, but I have a few coins left and I have friends near by.

TRAVELER: Well, let me give you a silver piece to help make good your loss.

STRANGER: No, sir, I will not take it, I thank you. But it would be best if you hurried on to the town to tell the justices, and perhaps the watch will be able to take these miserable robbers.

TRAVELER: I will do as you say, but I am afraid such sturdy fellows will not be easy to catch. Are you well now? How are your hurts? Here, take some more of my medicine.

STRANGER (*taking drink and handing back flask*): Well enough, sir, I thank you. In a few minutes I will be able enough to walk again.

TRAVELER: Very well, I will leave you. If you should need me again, ask for me at the sign of the Angel in Mulcaster.

STRANGER: Very good, sir. The sign of the Angel. I will remember. I thank you, sir. You have been like a good angel to me this day. Fare you well.

TRAVELER: Farewell, old man. Let us hope these rogues will be taken!

TRAVELER *goes*.

STRANGER: Ay, let us hope so.

He sits up straight, dusts down his cloak, pulls out the TRAVELER's *purse and begins counting over the money.* ROBIN *re-enters from behind the hedge and sits down beside him.*

ROBIN: Was not that well done, Nick?

STRANGER: Ay, well enough. But next time, remember, you need not cudgel me so hard.

ROBIN: Must we not do it life-like? You said so yourself.

STRANGER: I am not so sure we did well to rob this fellow so near the city. He has gone to tell the magistrates. We have escaped them so far, but one of these days we shall be too clever. Perhaps we should do well to leave the city alone tonight.

ROBIN: We will talk of that later. Now it is time for you to give me my share of the fellow's purse.

STRANGER: There is not much here, I fear.

ROBIN: Never mind, give me my share.

STRANGER: Well, here are two silver pieces for you. There.

He puts the purse away, after giving ROBIN *the coins.*

But come, Robin, I do not like your manner of speaking.

ROBIN: I do not like your manner of keeping the spoils to yourself.

STRANGER: What's this? Have I not taught you your trade? Am I not your father?

ROBIN: No, you are not my father. It is true you

have taught me my trade, but I have been a good pupil and brought you much profit.

STRANGER: You have cost me much to bring up, too. You are like my own son. Sons do not share their father's wealth while they are yet boys. You are mine, do you hear? I bought you from your father —he sold you to me. Why, I believe it was in this very place ten years ago that he and I made our bargain.

ROBIN: I do not care about that. I have heard it all before. You treat me like a child and keep my share of our winnings.

STRANGER: What is all this talk of your share? Do you not trust me? Come now, Robin, we have traveled far together. We have been friends, have we not? We have been partners.

ROBIN: You do not treat me like a partner, Nick.

STRANGER: Well, from now on I shall do so. Only you must trust me.

ROBIN: Trust you? Can anyone trust a thief?

STRANGER: Have I ever robbed you?

ROBIN: You robbed my father and mother.

STRANGER: I did not. It was a bargain. He sold you to me.

ROBIN: What did you pay him?

STRANGER: I paid him a purse of gold. What he did with it I know not. I need not have given him it, but I dealt with him honestly. I hoped it would keep his mouth shut.

ROBIN: Well, I do not care. This is all past now. I do not remember my father and mother.

STRANGER: Nor I neither. Come, we are friends and partners now. We must not stay talking here, or the traveler will find he has been robbed and come back to look for us. Let us go separately.

ROBIN: Shall we meet tonight?

STRANGER: I think we may. These city watchmen are clumsy fellows and we are not known here. It is ten years since I was in Mulcaster. We will call on our honest shopkeeper tonight and leave the city tomorrow.

ROBIN: What time tonight?

STRANGER: The moon will be going down by twelve. I will meet you at twelve. You know where the place is?

ROBIN: Yes I heard the two women in the inn say it was a little shop beside the market—a little shop, they said, but full of silver and pewter dishes and such fine wares. It is kept badly by an old doddering fool who will give us no trouble.

STRANGER: Good. (*He gets up to go.*) Let us go and get food. I will meet you in the graveyard by the cathedral church.

ROBIN: In the graveyard. A little before midnight. Fare you well.

STRANGER: Farewell. And remember, boy—trust me.

He goes.

ROBIN: Yes, I will trust you, Nick—(*muttering*) as I would trust the devil. (*Goes off in the opposite direction.*)

SCENE II

The same evening. Before the curtain goes up, Mulcaster Cathedral clock begins to chime eight. Before it has finished the curtain rises on the interior of JOHN CATCHPOLE'S *new shop in Mulcaster. A lamp is burning. It is a more prosperous-looking room than the former one, with a cloth on the table, imposing chairs to sit on, a side table with silver mugs and tankard. There are pewter and silver dishes, and other articles on shelves. A window, an outside door and an inner door.* BARNEY *is whistling cheerfully as he polishes some silver and puts it back on the shelves. He finishes with the silver, goes to the side table, puts the tankard and two mugs on the tray, carries them to the table, then stops whistling as a loud, official knock is heard on the door. He replaces the tray on the side table and goes to open the door.*

BARNEY: Who's there?
WATCHMAN (*outside*): Open up! It's the constable!

BARNEY *opens the door and admits the* WATCHMAN.

WATCHMAN: What is your name?

BARNEY: Barnard Antony Nicholas Simon Pomfret, so please you.

WATCHMAN: That's as may be. Is this your shop?

BARNEY: Nay, it's not my shop.

WATCHMAN: Then what are you doing here, Barnard Antony Nicho——

BARNEY: You may call me Barney, Constable. My master calls me Barney—and other things beside.

WATCHMAN: Who is your master?

BARNEY: Why, Master Catchpole, that sells silverware and pewterware and all such ware. Do you not know him?

WATCHMAN: That's as may be. Tell your master to watch his shop well and make all fast. There are thieves about the city.

BARNEY: Ay, that there are. You may see them in the market, minding fruit stalls and butter stalls and all manner of stalls.

WATCHMAN: These be honest thieves, Master Barney. But there are unhonest thieves about likewise.

BARNEY: My master will have nothing to do with that sort, Constable. He has had nothing to do with thieves since his little boy was stolen away these many years since. Have you seen these common, disrespectable, non-charitable thieves you speak of?

WATCHMAN: No, for they be little acquainted with us constables. But a traveler that came into the city not three hours ago has told the magistrates how he was cheated of his purse upon the highroad by an old rascally man who said he had been set upon by knaves.

BARNEY: Dear, oh dear! What with knaves, thieves, murderers, cheats, rascals and other such misreputable fellows, this is no place for honest thieves like us poor folk.

WATCHMAN: That's as may be. And so, Master Barney, I come to warn you and tell you to keep a good watch. Now I must go. (*Eyeing the cider.*) It's a cold night to be out in.

BARNEY: That's why I stay indoors—and my master too, who is coming in any minute to take a mug of cider. Why don't you stay indoors, Master Constable?

WATCHMAN: That is against regulations. But it would not be against regulations for a constable, if a kind neighbor were to offer him a mug of cider, to take such a mug of cider and consume it. Do you understand me?

BARNEY: Oh, would you like a mug of cider? Now why didn't you ask for it? (*He pours out a mug and hands it to the* WATCHMAN.)

WATCHMAN: Why, it would not be mannerly to do that, but since you give it me, I think I may take it. (*He drinks the mug in one draught and returns it.*) Your health, Master Barney, and I thank you. A quiet night to you, and farewell. Tell your master I will keep an eye on his shop. (*He goes out.*)

BARNEY: Farewell to you, Constable. A most civil and honest constable. (*He puts the tray on the table, after substituting a fresh mug.* JOHN *comes in, followed by* KATE.)

JOHN: Who was that, Barney?

BARNEY: A constable of the watch, master. He came to tell us to look out for thieves.

JOHN: They are lazy wasters, these constables. I believe he came in to beg a cup of my cider. And he would have taken it, had you given him it, Barney.

BARNEY: Oh do you think so, master? But this was a very honest, civil constable, who told me we should not trouble ourselves, for he would keep his eyes open and see that we are not robbed.

JOHN: Nor shall we be, unless he robs us himself. Have you shut up the chickens, Barney?

BARNEY: Ay, just as I always do.

JOHN: Just as you always do! That's what I feared. Well, you are honest, Barney, which is more than most folks are nowadays. You shall have a mug of cider with us before you go to bed. (*He pours out three mugs.* JOHN *and* KATE *sit down at the table.* BARNEY *drinks his standing.*)

BARNEY: Here's health to us, and long life.

KATE: I want no long life. I have lived too long already.

They all drink.

JOHN: Well, there is one thing about selling metalware instead of earthenware. You can not break my goods as you used to, Barney.

BARNEY: That is true, sir, but I do my best. This silverware, though, takes a deal of cleaning and polishing. I must be up early, so I will bid you both good night.

He puts down his cup and goes.

JOHN: Good night, Barney.

KATE: Good night. (*Both drink.*)

JOHN: How prettily the moonlight shines upon my silver, Kate. Do you see it?

KATE: It does but make me think of thieves. It is a cold night and my rheumatism troubles me. Though 'tis not so bad as neighbor Martin's. A terrible thing is the——

JOHN: Now, cheer up, Kate. Things are not so bad.

KATE: I have nothing to be cheerful for.

JOHN: Indeed, you have. You have better clothes. We have more to eat and drink. We have not done so badly. Come, have some more cider.

KATE: Not tonight. It does my rheumatism no good. Nothing will ever do me good now. How long is it, John?

JOHN: How long?

KATE: Yes. How long is it since—since we lost our little child?

JOHN: Ten years, my dear. Yes, it is just ten years. The lad will be turned seventeen.

KATE: Seventeen or seven—it makes no difference now he is in the grave.

JOHN: Do not say so, Kate. There is no proof that the lad is dead.

KATE: How can you talk like that? Why have we never heard a word of him?

JOHN: We searched high and low, and the magistrates ordered a search made, and the town criers and heralds went out over the whole countryside. But what could they do for poor folks like us? Now, if we had been rich and prosperous then——

KATE: Well, we have prospered since, as you say. Little good has it done us. More care, more worry, more fine things to mind and clean, but no better sleep at night and no more rest for our bones.

JOHN: Get your bones to bed, wife. You have much to thank God for. Come.

He takes the lamp. She gets up, putting the tray on the side table.

KATE: Yes, there is no sense in sitting here. I do not like this new shop like the old one.

JOHN: Nonsense! It is a fine shop. It is clean and dry and as pretty a shop as any in Mulcaster.

KATE: Have you locked up well? There is no trusting that poor Barney.

JOHN: Yes, I have barred and bolted the door.

KATE: Well, it's no matter, for there is nothing in the shop I would mind losing now.

KATE *goes out, followed by* JOHN *with the lamp.*

Curtain falls to indicate passing of an hour or so.

The clock strikes ten and the curtain rises, just before it finishes. ROBIN *appears at the window furtively, silhouetted against the moonlight. The inner door slams, and another door beyond it.* ROBIN *tries the outer door and finds it bolted. He fiddles with the window catch, unfastens it, slips inside and stands for a moment looking round. He listens, then closes the window, and quietly unbolts the door to make sure that he can escape from it if disturbed. He is carrying a large bag. Into this he places the silver objects he begins to collect as he goes rapidly round the room from shelf to shelf, muttering to himself.*

ROBIN: All's quiet . . . Silver . . . Silver . . . Pewter—too heavy . . . Nice pair of plates.

The heavy tread of the WATCHMAN *is heard, and the* WATCHMAN *himself appears outside the window, humming a tune. He stops, glances in at the shop window, while* ROBIN *cowers back into the shadow, then passes on out of earshot.* ROBIN'S *breath escapes loudly. He continues round the shop.*

ROBIN: Brass . . . silver—pretty thing, that . . . copper . . . pewter . . . What's this?

He stops to examine a silver object, and is so ab-

*sorbed that he does not notice the outer door open
silently behind him. Enter the* STRANGER, *who
comes swiftly up behind* ROBIN, *places his hand
over his mouth and clutches his arm. The following
conversation takes place in a hoarse whisper.*

STRANGER: You young dog, you thought to steal a
march on me, eh?

ROBIN (*struggling*): Let me go!

STRANGER: But I followed you. I guessed you would
be up to no good. Thought you'd get here first and
make off with the goods, did you?

ROBIN (*pulling* STRANGER'S *hand from his mouth*):
I'm tired of robbing for you, Nick. I am setting up
on my own now. So let me go, do your hear! I'm
finished with you.

STRANGER: Quiet! Do you want to wake the house?
Come, let's find a safer place to talk.

ROBIN: I don't care. I'm done with you, I say. (*He
breaks free and runs to the door, dropping his bag
and knocking over the table. He opens the door,
then closes it hastily.*)

STRANGER: You young fool! Now what have yo
done?

ROBIN: It's too late. There's no escape. That fat
stable is only a little way down the street.
rouse the city.

Enter from the inner door BARNEY *in b*

*sleeves with a lamp which he puts down on the side
table.*

BARNEY: Why, masters, what are you doing here at
this time? You rogues, what are you doing with my
master's silver? Help, master, we are robbed! Help,
help! Thieves, thieves!

During this speech the STRANGER *runs at him
with a brass candlestick and knocks him down.*

STRANGER: Come, Robin, we must get away from
here, constable or no constable!

He runs out of the door. Meanwhile the WATCH-
MAN *has run past the window and seizes the*
STRANGER *on the threshold. He forces him back into
the room, giving him a blow with his truncheon
~~~d grasping him by the back of the neck.* JOHN
~~~rs from the inner door. He is wearing a night-
~~~d dressing gown.* BARNEY *has struggled to*

all this noise? My wife is sleeping.
~~~ happened?
~~~ this fellow running from your
~~~wler. Keep your hands down,

r. It is a plain thief. And
~~~d them putting your sil-

STRANGER: Robin, why are you standing there? Come to my help and rid me of this fat fool——

BARNEY: Robin, Robin? Why, that was my master's child's name that was stolen these——

JOHN (*approaching the* STRANGER): Why, where have I seen you before, you devil!

BARNEY: You are just such a young fellow as my master's boy would be!

WATCHMAN: I must take both of these men and put them behind bars till the justices examine them in the morning.

JOHN: No, stay a minute, friend. I must talk with these men.

WATCHMAN: Master Barney, get me a rope that I may tie up this old devil, or he will escape me.

BARNEY *goes out of the inner door.*

JOHN: Come, sir, are you not the old devil who stole my son ten years age? Answer me, you thieving vagabond.

BARNEY *returns with a rope, followed by* KATE, *in night wear with a shawl round her.*

WATCHMAN: Give me the rope. Sit down there, dog!

The WATCHMAN *and* BARNEY *tie the* STRANGER *to chair.*

KATE: Husband, what is all this clamor? And who are

these men? I am scared out of my wits. We shall all be murdered in our beds. I thought——

JOHN: These fellows were found robbing the shop, Kate. Barney and the constable have caught them with my silver in their bag. How they got in is more than I can say.

WATCHMAN: If you will guard this fellow, Master Catchpole, I will step across to the Angel and see if I can find the man who informed against a highway rogue this afternoon. He is lodging there. I will not be an instant.

    The WATCHMAN *goes out.*

JOHN: We will mind them, Constable. Speak now, you old curmudgeon. Who are you? Are you not the man who told me he was the devil and stole my boy?

BARNEY: Yes, speak, evil one, or I will hit you over the head with a candlestick, the way you hit me. No, two candlesticks.

STRANGER: I have little to say. I see you are John Catchpole who used to sell pottery dishes and mugs in Bullfinch Lane. I did not know that you had taken another shop. This is your son Robin——

KATE: Robin!

JOHN: My son!

STRANGER: But I did not steal him. You gave him to me. Or rather, you sold him. Is this not true, Catchpole?

ROBIN: Are you my father, and did you sell me, like he said?

JOHN: No, it is not true. You cheated me.

STRANGER: You did well out of the bargain. Where are the gold coins I left you?

JOHN: I will give you them again, and more beside. You shall not have my boy a minute longer.

STRANGER: Have you nothing to say, Robin? Have I not brought you up, and fed you and clothed you? Have we not lived together, and traveled together, stolen together, and robbed together—ay, and been caught together and lain in the same prison?

The WATCHMAN *comes in with the* TRAVELER.

Have you nothing to say to me now? Will you leave me to rot and perish as if I had never known you?

WATCHMAN: That's as may be. Now, by your leave, Master Catchpole, this is the gentleman as was robbed on the Mulcaster road this afternoon. I have brought him here to see if he knows this fellow for the rogue that robbed him.

JOHN: Good evening, sir.

TRAVELER: Good evening to you. Yes, Officer, this is the man. I order you to arrest him and have him charged with highway robbery.

WATCHMAN: He shall come with me, and you must appear before the magistrates tomorrow to inform

against him. You had best come too, Master Catchpole.

The WATCHMAN *unties the* STRANGER *and hauls
him to his feet.*

STRANGER: This young rogue must go with me. He
was in it as deep as I.

WATCHMAN (*to the* TRAVELER): Have you seen this
young man before?

TRAVELER (*examining* ROBIN): No, I have not. Never
set eyes on him. So if you'll excuse me, I'll be going.
Good night to you all.

The TRAVELER *goes.*

WATCHMAN: Good night, sir. All the same, Master
Catchpole, I'm afraid I must take your son along
with me—if he is your son, though how a son of
yours comes to be such a vagrant and a sneak-by-
night, if I may say so, why, that is more than I can
understand.

KATE: Oh, do not take my son, Master Constable. He
is no thief, that I'll swear.

ROBIN: Yes, mother—if you are my mother—I am a
thief, and a good one too. That fellow there, Nick,
learned me my trade.

KATE: Oh Robin, do not say so, for I am sure you
will never steal again.

STRANGER: Ah, you whining young devil, have you
nothing——

WATCHMAN: Be quiet, you. Save your breath for the justices.

JOHN: See here, Constable. If you will leave this young man with me tonight, I'll go bail for him, and I warrant he shall appear before the justices in the morning. (*He takes out a purse.*) Here is ten pounds, Constable. Will you take that as bail?

WATCHMAN: I think I may do that, sir. (*Takes purse, counts money and puts it in his pocket.*) This is a young fellow and maybe the justices will not be hard on him, specially if he is the son of a decent citizen like you, sir.

JOHN: Well, Robin, you must choose between this old rascal and your father.

BARNEY: Choose your father, Robin; he is the best old rascal, when all's said. Stay with your father and your mother and your friend Barney that used to tell you stories and riddles in the times gone by.

ROBIN: I will stay with my father and mother if they will have me. I owe you nothing, Nick, but the learning of a bad trade which I must now unlearn.

STRANGER: A curse upon you for a——

WATCHMAN: Quiet you! Come, we must to jail.

JOHN: If your duty allows it, Constable, I wish you would take a mug of cider before you go.

JOHN *pours cider and he and* BARNEY *hand it round.*

WATCHMAN: Thank you sir, it is a cold night, and I mind not if I don't and mind not if I do.

JOHN: There. I warrant you have not tasted cider like that before now.

BARNEY *and the* WATCHMAN *look at each other significantly*.

WATCHMAN: That's as may be sir, that's as may be.

CURTAIN